Just the One

Just the One

Richard Ingrams & John Wells
Illustrated by Brian Bagnall

PRIVATE EYE/ANDRE DEUTSCH

Published in Great Britain by Private Eye Productions Ltd,
6 Carlisle Street, London W1

© 1986 Pressdram Ltd
Illustrations by Brian Bagnall © 1986

ISBN 233 97984 0

Printed by The Bath Press, Bath
Typeset by JH Graphics Ltd, Reading

10 Downing Street
Whitehall

12 JULY 1985

Dear Bill,

I wouldn't say this lightly or to anyone apart from your good self, but I have been seriously considering whether it wouldn't be a good idea if M. took a leaf out of poor Princess Michael's book and committed herself to the King Edward VIIth Hospital For Nervous Officers for a spell of complete rest in a darkened room. (I would of course appear on television every night to reassure the nation that she was perfectly well and not giving the warders any trouble at all.)

Seriously, Bill, it is bloody worrying. She got back from Milan still trembling with rage, kicking doors and shouting incoherently at anyone who came near her. Of course, if it was you or I, a couple of large ones in the peace of the Saloon Bar would soon restore the equilibrium. But the trouble with the Boss is that she has no such spiritual resources to fall back on. In our case again, a couple of weeks in the Algarve perched on the rafia barstools of Myrtle Flack would restore a light to the eye and a spring to the step. Not so M., and even the wall to wall luxury and in-house psychiatrist of Schloss Bangelstein will serve little purpose, as she can never take the weight off her feet and spends all day ringing people up and sending them memos.

In one of her lucid moments I did try to find out what had gone wrong at the Eurosummit. She mentioned Kohl and Mitterand, and then it was Krakatoa as per usual, with D.T. legging it down the slopes a hair's breadth ahead of the molten tide. I can only think that for once Monsieur le Frog was not slobbering over her hand and may even have had the temerity to answer back.

Matters have not been improved by the news from the Brecon Beacons by-election, where our man minced in some hours after the other candidates had breasted the tape. Here in the Bunker they're doing their best to explain it away as midsummer madness, though feeble attempts were made at the last minute by the Goebbels Department to call up the spectre of A. Scargill

'. . . *advertising campaigns by the Corsican brothers . . .*'

Esquire (eyes glazed and pockets bulging with Moscow Gold) as the crazed puppet-master manipulating Mr Woodentop Kinnock. But all to no avail. Letters have now been dispatched to the usurers asking for long loans to underwrite a new series of thousand-bomber advertising campaigns by the Corsican Brothers.

The long-awaited reshuffle has yet to be finalised, but the Boss's mind is still haunted by hopes of the Golden Youth who went away in disgrace holding his trousers up with one hand – Smarmy Cecil to you and me. You may have seen her, when questioned by that ghastly little creep Frost on the Sunday morning TV, saying 'He must come back, he must come back, he knows how to run a business, he started at the bottom and worked his way up.' I said to her in the hospitality room afterwards that he certainly had started at the bottom in more ways than one, and that if running your own business was going to be a passport to Cabinet Office, why didn't she bring in Maurice Picarda, who had built up more small businesses than Parkinson had had hot candlelit dinners.

Mercifully, perhaps, Margaret did not seem to hear and continued to murmur 'He must come back, he must come back . . .' reminding me sharply of that very nice old biddy Mrs Waddilove-Stokes whose boy went missing in the trenches and who always met the Boat Train with a bunch of flowers. You can't argue with that kind of thing. Just give them an arm round the shoulder and talk about the weather.

Good news from Furniss, by the way. I took him a bottle of British sherry that Maurice picked up in the Duty Free on the way back from the Isle of Man, and he was very chipper about the nest egg. Apparently Lawson has finally seen the light about Interest Rates and is sticking steadfastly to 14% or thereabouts for the duration. This, apparently, is 'to keep inflation down', though as usual with our Fat Friend over the Fence it is hard to follow the logic of it. A welcome bonus nonetheless for the small saver like you and me with a couple of million tucked away on deposit.

Short of the Edward VIIth Scenario going into production I am not too sanguine about your proposed Tour of the Highland Distilleries, tempting though it sounds. We are booked into the Widow Glover's Dracula Suite for the customary three weeks in August. A Three Line Whip I think, as far as yours truly is concerned, a group of Swiss Bankers featuring on the bill of attractions. God help us all.

See you at the Club on Tuesday with or without the Major.

Yours aye,

DENIS

P.S. Had you thought of dropping in on Scroggie outside Inverness? He gets very lonely on his own.

10 Downing Street
Whitehall

26 JULY 1985

Dear Bill,

Sorry to miss you at Sandwich, but I got mixed up with a lot of globe-trotting Yankee lawyers who wanted to have a drink in the Mermaid in Rye so they could tell the folks back home about it. Who should be propping up the Mayflower Bar but Batty Dugdale, out on parole from the clinic. If you met him for the first time you'd think he was quite sane, but I could see a nasty light in his eye when one of our American cousins ordered orange juice, and he began to growl just like he did that night at the Rotary. The Manager seemed to know the form and said it was time for walkies, so I volunteered to steer him back to his digs. By that stage it was pouring with rain and as far as I can remember I decided to call it a day.

When I got to town I discovered that the US Law Society were everywhere. Even when I popped down to Ivan's for my regular short back and sides and buff-up on top, there was a party of them with name-badges in their lapels all peering in at me through the window as if I was something at the Zoo. Ivan went out into the street with his cut-throat razor and told them all to bugger off, but they only laughed and made jokes about the Demon Barber of Jermyn Street.

'. . . Batty Dugdale, out on parole from the clinic . . .'

In the chair the conversation inevitably turned to poor old Hoppo's operation, for which his compatriots seemed to have scant time as they whooped it up amid the bright lights. Ivan very wisely observed that all this anxiety about the old boy's ability to govern being affected by his state of health was clearly misplaced, as the US of A had been on automatic pilot ever since they lowered him into the cockpit, and all he had to do was smile and wave from time to time. The fact that he'd had some of his insides out wouldn't make a blind bit of difference as long as he could occasionally focus on his prompting screen and go on waving and saying 'Have a nice day' to anyone who passed across his field of vision. The Boss however got a bit weepy and sent off £25 worth of Herbaceous Mixture via Interflora with a personally scribbled Get Well Soon card. Wandering through her study en route for the cellar I found her dabbing her eyes over a silver-framed photograph of the Old Cowboy and his wizened co-star inscribed 'Eternally Yours, Ronald and Nancy'.

'He is a dear, dear man, Denis,' she intoned, 'and the future of us all rests upon his shoulders. Let us pray he will be spared.' I observed a two-second silence before proceeding on my vital errand.

If you ask me, the dark clouds over our future are probably gathering rather nearer home. Lawson is running round in circles telling everyone not to panic, pound going through the roof, all the same old arguments being trotted out back to front as when it was going through the floor, this is a good thing for British Exports etc. Meanwhile most of our hard-earned deposits, it transpires, have been entrusted to a bucket-shop outfit known as Johnson-Matthey run by various ex-associates of Maurice Picarda from the days when he dabbled in the rag trade in Birmingham and who have now gone to ground on the Costa del Sol cocking a snook at the massed ranks of Smellysocks who howl for their blood. The Corsican Brothers' answer to these and other so-called hiccups is to play the Moscow Gold Card. Poor old Howe was instructed to brush the dust off his brothel creepers, get up on his hind legs, and reveal the sinister plot, with Mr Nice Guy Gingernuts Kinnock unmasked as the Wolf in Sheep's Clothing, and Scargill with his hand up his arse working the teeth. Obviously old Howe didn't really have his heart in the script, so its effect was somewhat muffled.

The only other shot in the locker as I hinted in my last is a return by popular demand of Matinee Idol Cecil P. Mr P., aware of my wife's keen enthusiasm for his work, has been putting it about that he could just be tempted out of retirement if a suitable role were to be found for him, but he must have an answer before too long or he will be obliged to take up other offers – of which, Mr P. has not been slow to point out, there has been no shortage. According to him, there is hardly a multinational in the country that is not clamouring for his presence in the boardroom. Such overtures have not been too rapturously received by the older hands in the Casting Department. Willie Whitelaw told me at Sandwich that the fear had been expressed in some quarters of a lone figure appearing outside Number Ten Downing Street, pushing a pram up and down the pavement and brandishing a placard demanding justice for unmarried mothers.

Incidentally I have just heard that the American lawyers got their just deserts for grinning at me in the barber's. They had to sit through an hour of the Boss at the Albert Hall, followed by an hour and a half of Hailsham wittering on in his decaying robes surrounded by a cloud of moths.

Yours aye,

DENIS

10 Downing Street
Whitehall

9 AUGUST 1985

Dear Bill,

Just a quick line before we hang the Swissair tags on our Duty Free and jet off to Gnomeland.

As you will have seen in the *Daily Telegraph,* the term at Halitosis Hall ended with the usual high spirits and vandalism, all because somebody in Whitehall had the bright idea of jacking Hailsham's pay up to seventy-five grand a year – not a large emolument in this day and age – but considering all he does is doze on the Woolsack sneezing and scratching his arse from time to time it was hardly to be wondered at that there should be some angry murmurs from the Proles. You can't rely on our lot either nowadays, even in support of a fair day's pay for a fair day's work. The Wets predictably hollered a lot of SDP rubbish, got pissed and trailed off through the wrong lobby.

The Boss blew her top over this, and actually threatened to resign, in my view never a good card to play. Witness the melancholy tale of poor old Wino Henderson at Burmah. As you may recall he was reprimanded after some malfeasance at the Christmas Party and stormed into the boardroom to say he'd never been so insulted, his private life was his own affair, and he was tendering his resignation forthwith. Blow me, when he got back on Monday morning expecting the red carpet and the Entertainments Officer Fernley-Whittingstall on his knees pleading for forgiveness, they'd walled his office up and turned it into the Ladies' Wash Room. Luckily for the Boss, her ploy seems to have succeeded and Hailsham's pay rise has gone through, although the old boy has announced he's going to give it all to Oxfam. Rum world, eh?

Hopalong is apparently falling to bits, which I suppose was only to be expected. The latest scare was when he noticed his nose had turned a funny colour and insisted on taking a bit of it to the doctor's to be looked at under a magnifying glass. You or I could have told him that a shiny red nose is perfectly normal in anyone over the age of forty, but these Americans are all obsessed about their health and rush off to the medic on the slightest pretext. That is why Dr O'Gooley, whose own nose actually glows in the dark, so often talks about toddling over there and upping his salary by six or eight noughts.

I hope you managed to sell your Krugerrands in time. I got a tip from the Portuguese woman who cleans at Number 11 that our Fat Friend in the Waistcoat had been on the blower to the Cape and that things sounded pretty grisly. Furniss very decently unloaded mine in about ten minutes on some unsuspecting mutt from Kuwait. A p.c. from Mrs Van der Kafferbesher asking for food parcels told a pretty poignant tale. Apparently Brer Coon has finally put his foot down and is refusing to buy any more Water Biscuits and Mature Cheddar from the local Safeway's with the result that Mrs Van der K's friends in trade are having to put the shutters up. The Boss I think has remained pretty sound on S.A., insisting on business as usual, confidence in an expanding market, and the best way to bring Mr Botha to see reason is to do nothing at all. Meanwhile Botha, ignoring the wishes of miscellaneous busybodies all round the world, very

'. . . noticed his nose had turned a funny colour . . .'

wisely decided to wield the big stick and arrest the clergy, in my
opinion the true niggers in the woodpile, with Moscow chipping
in prettily heavily whenever the collecting plate goes round. Mrs
Van der K. told me last time I was down there that this Bishop
Tutu man who is always being garlanded with Swedish peace
prizes is actually a close friend of Mr Gorblimov and is always
going off for free holidays on the Black Sea. None of that has been
in the paper, obviously, but Mrs Van der K. has her ear pretty
close to the ground, and it made me wonder whether Runcie isn't
up to some nonsense of that kind too. (You saw he sent one of his
minor sky-pilots out to that agitator's funeral.)

For once I thought Brittan acted in a statesmanlike way in
bringing the pinkoes of Lime Grove to heel over this IRA Party

Political they were planning. Not that it would have made a blind bit of difference as all the viewers are plastered by that hour of the night. But it was high time somebody made it clear that there is a limit to the sort of bare-faced cheek Margaret has to listen to day after day on the wireless and TV from assorted shirt-lifters and Trotskyites masquerading as entertainment. Incidentally after all this guff from M. about oxygen and violence which she got from MacGregor during a somewhat rambling lunch when the talk turned to putting out fires on oil rigs – entre nous, the old geezer is now very over-ripe for the Farm – where was I? Anyway Hurd, our mastermind in Belfast, announced last week that the IRA were running out of steam, and within seconds you could hardly hear him speak for the noise of Best US TNT blowing comestibles into the street all over the Province. I suppose that sort of prat learns his lesson eventually.

When you receive your annual p.c. of the Matterhorn you may find the message a little cryptic as all the post is opened and read by Dr Bosendorfer, the in-house shrink. For 'weather conditions' read M., for 'gentians in short supply this year' read the inevitable drought, and 'having a lovely time' draw your own conclusions. My best to Mrs Flack and all the gang under the thatched bar on the beach. You lucky buggers.

Yrs by a thread,

DENIS

Salzburg, Austria

23 AUGUST 1985

Dear Bill,

Sorry I had to leave the country before I had a chance to show you over the new Chateau Thatcher SE 19. I think you'll like it eventually, though at the time of writing it's only a hole in the ground. The big plus about starting from scratch is that one can dictate certain custom-built variants to the basic design, to wit, in

'. . . and have a look at the show house . . .'

my own case, a secret bomb-proof hideaway for 'private papers',
with underground venue for perusal of same, camp bed for
sleeping off effects etc.

You may be wondering why we have sunk five hundred grand
into this detached luxury residence in a highly sought-after
suburban area when, as things stand, it looks as though M. will
be snug as a bug in a rug at Number Ten for the duration.
Thereby, as they say, hangs a tale.

I don't know whether you remember Maurice's friend
Sharples who went bust in scrap metal through no fault of his
own. I happened to bump into both of them in the Club after
lunch a couple of months back having spent a frustrating
morning with Furniss trying to make sense of interest rates over
several bottles of his Amontillado Molto Repulsivo. Sharples and

Maurice were examining some very flashy-looking architects' plans for this new estate, it being Maurice's thought that he might subcontract for the conservatory-cum-patio area in some of the de-luxe Ambassador Club models.

It transpires that Sharples has clawed his way back to respectability and is quite a big noise on the Estate Agency scene down in Dulwich. 'Let me ask you a question, Squire,' he said to me, wiping the froth off his moustache. 'What are you doing with your money? I understand from Morrie here that you've got quite a nice little nest-egg stashed away. NatWest, did Morrie say?' Plainly our mutual drinking companion had been his usual discreet self apropos my private finances. 'Say no more,' our shiny friend continued, gesturing expansively to old Havergal at the bar, 'these gents will have the same again, only trebles. There's only one safe place to have your money these days, Den, especially with your chum Nigel playing silly-buggers with our hard-earned LSD – not a friend of yours, I trust? – and that is Bricks and Mortar. Cheers.'

Quite frankly, Bill, I had not taken an immediate shine to the fellow, but his line on El Waistcoat, our obese neighbour, struck a chord, and from then on we got on like a couple of snorts in an optic. Before long Sharples said why didn't we climb into the back of his Porsche, shoot down to Dulwich and have a look at the Show House.

No sooner said than done, despite the rain bucketing down, and after a bit of argy-bargy about getting the keys when the office was shut we were traipsing round this exceedingly commodious residence, situated as Sharples had very cleverly omitted to mention, within a chip-shot of the First Green, ballproof double-glazing all included.

Next morning I was surprised to read in the paper that I had bought it. It was the Boss who drew my attention to the item some time before I had entirely come to. Just as I was about to explain, Barratt's were on the blower thanking us for our custom and saying they had organised a photo-call for the world's press to record M's impressions of her new Quality Home of Distinction.

The Management proved predictably volcanic at all this – What the bloody hell did I think I was doing? Was I trying to signal to Kinnock and Scargill that Downing Street was looking for a new tenant? And variations on this theme. For once I stood my ground against the molten lava, quoting Sharples' safe-as-houses line, though omitting any slanderous reference to Nicely

Nicely next door. I also reminded her that Barratt had been very decent about chipping into the Party Funds, and the least she could do in return was to give them a publicity snap.

Hence M's sullen appearance in a pair of borrowed wellingtons at the site, where I thought she concealed her irritation on learning that the foundations remained to be laid remarkably well all things considered.

Now it is my turn to sulk. As I explained we were all set for the annual three weeks of purgatory chez the widow Glover. However, at the very last minute the good lady was struck down by some unspecified 'bug' and full of effusive regrets having to cancel. If you ask me the only thing that bugged her was the thought of M.& D.T. arriving with the usual barrowload of confidential files to camp on her premises for two weeks of peak holiday time. My rapture at the cancellation was short-lived however, it transpiring that the Widow G. had fixed us up at short notice with a very dear Austrian friend of hers, Herr Kundell, owner of a delightful hunting lodge deep in the forests. She added that we would be pleased to hear that Herr Kundell was like ourselves a great music lover and had already booked seats at several opera performances in Salzburg. Before ringing off the Widow said she had a hot tip for Margaret from her friend Herr Schocke-Muller, who apparently advises her on her investments from the Other Side.

He particularly wanted Margaret to know that real estate was grotesquely over-valued throughout the Western World and the only sane course was to go liquid and take advantage of high interest rates.

Auf Wiedersehen

DENIS

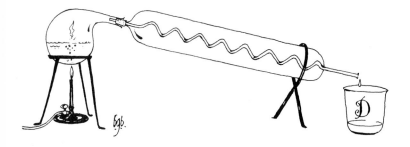

10 Downing Street
Whitehall

6 SEPTEMBER 1985

Dear Bill,

Did you get my p.c. from Salzburg? I thought you'd like the cherry-nosed old buffer pouring beer into his Lederhosen. According to our driver, the caption said 'It's all got a bit too hot for me in these parts!', an example of Boche humour to show that things haven't changed much when it comes to the Master Race and jokes.

As you may have gathered from my necessarily cryptic remarks, the Boss has developed an unaccountable thirst for culture. At first I thought it was some kind of lark dreamed up by the Saatchis to put the kibosh on the Philistine Image, but I have now rumbled the truth. You may recall that part of the indignities last year involved sitting through four hours of scraping and warbling called *The Demon Barber of Seville*. Something of that nature anyway. All these operas are very much the same: a lot of overweight nancy boys coming on in silly clothes and getting locked in the wardrobe. I think I may have nodded off in Act Two, but Margaret sat through the ballsaching farrago with eyes agleam, and afterwards the Widow G. took us behind the scenes to meet Herr von Karavan who had thought the whole bloody thing up.

Things backstage were pretty steamy, with the usual fleet of Berties in attendance rubbing him down, wiping his eye-shadow off, fetching him a dry wig etc. But as soon as he saw the Boss he sprang up in a very agile way for a seventy-year-old, slipped into a red velvet dressing gown and was soon slobbering over her hand. 'Ach, my Vunderlady!' he cried, sounding like the Commandant of Colditz after a major defection by the Wingcos all disguised as Old Mother Riley, 'so long I have worshipped at your feet!! I myself as you know have had my troubles, my Arthur Scargills in the Wind Section. But you and I, my Leader, we know how to deal with these Under-peoples! Zis offal, Bolshevik scum and vermin!'

Despite my lack of enthusiasm for long-haired musical weirdoes as a species and for the unspeakable tedium of the previous four

'. . . the Broadstairs Mantovani . . .'

hours of so-called entertainment, I had to agree that Karavan's view of the world seemed extremely sound, and I was not surprised this year when Margaret invited him to toddle over to our little fortified hunting lodge, with its barbed wire and lookout towers cunningly disguised as bird-watching hides, for a spot of Roast Venison. Here the friendship between Maestro and Megastar blossomed in no uncertain manner. It seems this Karavan has a very good record of locking out Orchestras. But he played his trump card when the name of E. Heath was unwisely dropped into the conversation by our landlord, Herr Heddbanger, who, during a lull, observed that Britain was fortunate to have musical Prime Ministers.

At this our guest's eyes narrowed, and forgetting our presence he relapsed into his native tongue. However, various familiar words linked to the name of our seafaring friend stood out with some clarity, including 'Dummkopf', 'Schweinhund' and 'Idiot'. When Karavan recovered himself sufficiently to break into English once again, it transpired that on more than one occasion, the blue-rinsed matelot had approached him, seeking his advice on conducting technique and pressing on him signed records and books inscribed 'From one Great Conductor to Another'. He went on to speak of the real distress of having to remain in his seat while the Broadstairs Mantovani had stumbled through 'one of our great masterpieces', and compared it to 'urinating on the grave of the Immortal Ludwig' – whoever that might be.

You did not have to be Sherlock Holmes to see that this excited harangue was going down a treat with the Old Lady. Her eyes shone, her lips parted in a moist smile and she gazed at the silver-haired bandleader with adoration that I have only seen equalled when Smarmy Cecil used to come round in one of his new suits with a bunch of flowers. I need hardly add that for the remainder of our so-called holiday we were press-ganged into the Dress Circle night after night to listen to the whole repertoire of brain-numbing cacophony produced over the years by our German Cousins.

Talking of Smarmy Cecil, you may have seen some speculation about Margaret's Autumn Shuffle. The only thing I can definitely give you by way of a betting tip is that the owl-eyed Wimp of the Remove, J. Selwyn Gummer, has finally got his cards, and not a moment too soon in my view. He was summoned down to Chequers yesterday afternoon, and arrived looking quite smug, clearly thinking that the invitation was to tea on the lawn and a Knighthood. Forty-five minutes in the Boss's study and he emerged a chastened figure. It was the first time I have ever felt a pang of sympathy for the little bugger, and I even offered him a scoop of Amazing Grouse to soothe his jangled nerves. This was clearly a mistake. His head came up at once, and giving me a scornful and dismissive glance, he said that he did not have to rely on chemical stimulants in moments of adversity. It was plainly God's plan that he should cease to be the Party Chairman, and from now on he would be able to devote himself more fully to putting the C. of E. back on the rails. I asked if he'd ever heard of someone called Archie Wellbeloved, in my view the only possible candidate to take over from Snaggleteeth at Canterbury, but at this he became even snootier and said that he didn't have to consult Skid Row on matters of ecclesiastical preferment.

Must close now, as I hear Fate knocking on the floor in the person of You Know Who.

Gung ho,

DENIS

P.S. When not stuffing herself with chocs in the front row of the Dress Circle, M. whiled away her few moments of free time in Austria glued to a frightful paperback she'd bought at the airport. It turns out it was written by a greedy little pill called Archer, who was drummed out of our lot some years back after something rather fishy on the business end of things. M. was so impressed by this penny dreadful that she is now thinking of bringing him back as an adviser. I pointed out that he and Cecil would make a pretty grisly double act as Yesterday's Spivs, hardly likely to inspire confidence in the punters. As far as Smarmy Cecil is concerned it looks as if my advice, for once, was heeded.

10 Downing Street
Whitehall

Dear Bill,

Sorry to hear that Maurice got caught up in the race riots in Birmingham. Apparently he had gone up there with his rep little Mr Deutsch to try and off-load a containerful of Rear Window Waving Hands which had fallen off the back of a supertanker onto some innocent trader. No sooner had they taken firm orders for half of the shipment than the bricks began to fly and his Cortina was a tangle of blazing metal. Probably a good thing, if you ask me, as he'd only bought it the week before from his dodgy friend in Sevenoaks and it hadn't been MOT'd.

I had a good laugh about Hurd, as I expect you did. The little greaser was just congratulating himself on having escaped unscathed from the Sharp End in Belfast, when hey presto the drug-crazed coons were pelting him with builders' materials in what was hitherto believed to be a reasonably salubrious backwater of Birmingham. At least it will teach him not to mince about for the benefit of the TV Cameras. There he goes, face all wreathed in compassionate smiles, begging the hordes to express their frustration, whereupon they take him at his word and shower him with masonry. (I've got it on video and watch it quite frequently whenever I need a chuckle.)

Apropos our new Home Secretary, he was obviously as surprised as we all were when he got the call. The whole shuffle, entre nous, was a bit of a botched job. Until the eleventh hour the Boss had been determined to bring in Smarmy C. whatever Tebbit, Whitelaw and even little Gummer might say against him. However, when I myself weighed in, showing Margaret a few of the postcards I had had from Cecil P. de Mille vaunting his own spectacular business opportunities on the back of saucy postcards from various foreign parts and offering me the loan of his holiday hideaway in the British West Indies any time I felt like getting plastered and tanned all over at one and the same time, she finally panicked and, with tears streaming down her face, drew a line through his name. As it turned out, we of the anti-CP brigade were proved right. No sooner were the names posted a week early in the changing rooms than little Miss Keays popped up on the front page of the gutter press, posing with her little Parkaninny and saying she wanted nothing more than to live a normal life away from the cameras. That sort of barmy woman never lets up, as the Major discovered when he divorced his third.

Once Parkie was dropped from the team, of course, there was a great deal of fairly desperate last-minute head-scratching. One of the casualties, I am happy to say, was that awful frizzy-haired chap Gowrie, for whom Margaret has always had an unaccountable penchant. He's never really appealed to me, quite honestly, with his lah-de-dah stuck-up ways and bow tie – always rabbiting on about some sub-human gorilla-faced loon in New York who earns a fortune pouring Dulux into the electric fan and then selling the curtains to a lot of pin-striped prats in Bond Street just like himself. No wonder he can't afford to live on his salary if he spends it on speculating in that kind of merchandise. All this meant M. frantically ringing round getting the poor buggers out of the bath and standing by the phone till she'd told the other one he'd got the shove. When the music stopped who should find himself without a cork seat but little cookie-pusher Brittan who I think Margaret had meant to make Foreign Secretary. I saw him on the stairs doing his best to look as though the Min. of Trade was what he'd wanted all his life, but I think I heard him burst into tears as he went round the corner.

To get her revenge on the anti-Parkinson brigade, M. insisted against all sager views on bringing in this ghastly male model Jeffrey Archer, who I think you met once at Brighton with a lot of rather seedy-looking advertising men raising money 'for charity'. His official position is Number Two to Mr Munster, and his brief is to go round the country raising morale amongst the woebegone rank and file. Can you imagine him at Daphne's Bring and Buy? He'd probably be given a cup of tea and asked to park round the back. I don't know if you've tried to read one of his books, but they're apparently done on one of those new-fangled machines where you press a button and it all comes out by the yard.

Boris is very miffed about all the Russkie diplomats being put on the boats for spying. He says, quite reasonably in my view, what else do we think they're here for. Moreover that this Mr Big who's just taken a golden bowler and free Warrington Vodka for life has been drawing double money for years and years, so what's all the fuss about? I said I'd pass the complaints on to Howe when

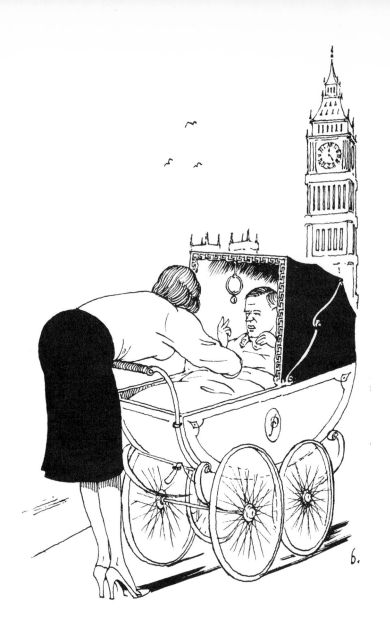

'. . . with her little Parkaninny . . .'

he got back from Nigeria, but he's been hors de combat after the pickled crabs he had in Lagos.

Roll on the Conference. I have ordered my bullet-proof vest and pant set from Lillywhite's and suggest you join us in the Maximum Security Block for a couple of large ones. For details see local press.

Yours pro tem,

DENIS

10 Downing Street
Whitehall

4 OCTOBER 1985

Dear Bill,

Sorry you weren't able to join us at Wentworth. As you may have heard on the grapevine, the Major, Maurice P. and Yours Truly got in a spot of trouble with the Club Secretary while witnessing Ballesteros' well-merited victory over the dozy Boche. It was pretty clear from the outset we weren't going to see much golf, so after a fairly heavy liquid luncheon in the Clubhouse we adjourned to what seemed a secluded copse and spread out the Major's tartan rugs for a spot of shut-eye. Next thing, wallop. Sharp cry of pain from Maurice as Langer's rather wild drive caught him unawares, waking him up in a flurry of oaths. Moments later the whole caravanserai of caddies, TV crews, spectators and finally the contestants arrived in the dingle to start poking about for the lost ball. Langer was pretty livid when it finally came to light in Maurice's plastic drinking beaker. I pressed a tenner into the Kraut's hand, hoping this would mollify him, but he got very shirty indeed and in the end we were hustled away like a bunch of vagrants.

Thank you for your congratulatory p.c. re my starring role in *The Treasurehouse of Memory — 500 Years at Number Ten* on BBC 1. Both of us were pretty reluctant to open the house to a bunch of overpaid Leftie riff-raff from the television, but Saatchis were most insistent; poor showing in polls, wonderful opportunity to portray the Boss in her role as housewife pottering around the kitchen, planning dinner menus etc, i.e. all the things

'. . . we adjourned to what seemed a secluded copse . . .'

she normally wouldn't touch with a bargepole. You may
remember they did the same thing for the Royals some time back,
and according to the Corsican Twins their ratings shot up as a
result. I only agreed to do it on the proviso that my den remained
out of bounds to the TV Berties, which was why you saw me
squatting on the settee opening a lot of poison pen letters Boris
would normally put straight into his shredder. Even then there
were the usual humiliations: having the top of one's head
plastered with pink make-up by some garrulous harpie, being
asked to say one's lines over and over again by a young jackass in
an open-necked shirt and leather jacket, and so on. According to
the Major I came over as not a bad understudy for Alf Garnett.
(Incidentally, why do they roar with laughter when he says
perfectly sensible things?)

As far as our Annual Shareholders' Meeting is concerned, the
Brothers and Mr Munster are pinning their hopes on the
Smellysocks making a hames of their show at Bournemouth this
week, leaving our lot to make their entrance looking like a decent

panto. At the moment things are going according to plan: Scargill, who has returned bronzed and fit from a two-week package trip to the Urals, his purse no doubt bulging with Moscow Gold, has got his teeth firmly locked in the Welshman's leg, insisting that when Ginger Nuts comes to power, a large share of the Budget is to be earmarked for the NUM Social and Christmas Fund. Meanwhile Comrade Hattersley has produced a ten-point plan to soak the rich, apparently under the impression that anyone on £20,000 a year is stinking and a natural enemy of the people, i.e. meet to be soaked. I can't see this going down too well in Finchley and areas South.

The current joke here at the Power House is that Hurd has now been in three times to ask for his old Ulster job back. Either that or insisting on danger money. Cookie-pusher Brittan always managed somehow to keep out of these things, but little Adolf Hurd seems to position himself for the custard pie every time. We anticipate a good turnout by the National Front at the Conference next week, and I personally shall be very cross if Margaret doesn't extend the hand of friendship to them in these troublous times. The Wets and Do-gooders meanwhile will set up their usual caterwauling, demanding the return of Lord Scarman, policemen in future to be armed only with feather dusters, and Brother Coon to be left to smoke his hemp in the peace and comfort of his own bomb-site. The chances of Hurd steering his craft between these two poles seem to me pretty remote.

Re Blackpool: I've had a definite acceptance from Maurice and the Major for drinks backstage: all my energies are likely to be sapped by the effort necessary not to sit next to wide-boy Jeffrey Archer. Gummer was bad enough with his ghastly tracts, but Archer's sales patter would bore the arse off an elephant.

Toodleoo,

DENIS

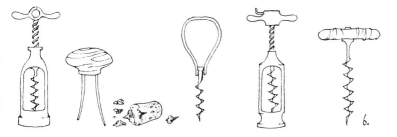

10 Downing Street
Whitehall

Dear Bill,

I am extremely sorry to hear that you both had such a disagreeable time with the Securicor boys at Blackpool. I explained to Maurice that badges had to be worn at all times, and that he would have to bring the special pass he got sent from Central Office the week before. Obviously what happened was that he had one of his amnesia spells in the bar on the train and probably handed it over to the guard in lieu of his ticket. It was additionally a mistake to claim to be an old friend of mine, as Sgt. Major Hardnutt told me he'd already dealt with a great many highly suspicious characters with strong Irish accents who had maintained the same thing. I think this was probably Dr O'Gooley and some of his private patients, but I haven't heard any confirmation of this from Harley Street.

I've been feeling a bit smug all through the week having warned the Powers That Be that they were making a great mistake in taking Roland Rat (a.k.a. J. Archer) on board. I knew that a prize pill like that would immediately go shooting his mouth off pretending to be a real politician and sure enough, just when everyone had agreed on a new compassionate approach to the unwaged, Brother Rat goes on the air quoting every word he'd heard me saying in the bar five minutes before. It's one thing to confide in Mine Genial Host and a few like-minded elbow-lifters that most of our income tax goes in subsidising a lot of work-shy yobboes hanging around street corners when they could be writing international best-sellers or starting their own window-cleaning business; quite another to go trumpeting it over the airwaves to the obvious distress of the Corsican Twins. Tebbit and the Boss came down on him like a ton of bricks after that and told him to put a sock in it, but it didn't seem to have the slightest effect and he went on bending the ear of any media person that moved and cluttering up the foyer of the hotel with dump bins of his paperback trash which he signed for those unfortunate punters who came within range. No wonder Gummer was floating about looking pretty smug, 'I told you so'

'. . . having had a heavy lunch with Oyster-eyes . . .'

written all over his holy Joe features. It's pretty humiliating to have to share any opinion with a squirt like that, which made me even crosser with Margaret for appointing Roland R. in the first place.

All in all it's been a good week for the D.T. Form Guide. Just imagine if Smarmy Cecil had been back on the platform with this latest Mills and Boon Bodice-Ripper coming out day after day in Maxwell's rag. The Boss would have looked pretty stupid. As things were, Saatchis were able to divert the reptiles to where the unsuspecting Lothario was attending a software conference north of the silvery Tay. In his absence we were even able to have a good chuckle over Colonel Keays's letter to M. about horsewhipping the bounder. Just as well the old boy didn't file my reply, written, I recall, rather late at night on RAC paper, pledging my full support for his campaign against 'an unspeakable cad' and speculating man to man on the unaccountable shine Margaret had taken to this human snake. The moral of the story is pretty obvious: A bit on the side, Straight down the slide. A lesson, alas, that Maurice has never learned, if the tatty-looking lady in the velvet dress he brought to Blackpool is anything to go by. He told me with great pride that she was a retired Traffic Warden from Matlock.

Apart from these excitements, the Conference turned out to be pretty good lead balloon time, the speakers all queuing up to try their hand at the Hit Kinnock on the Head and Ring the Bell Stall. This in the wake of Ginger's so-called triumph at Bournemouth, when he rounded on Scargill some three years after the horse had bolted. Mr Munster who was billed as the star turn for his hilarious warm-up act muffed all his lines, Madame Nigella was as usual cock-a-hoop, smugly predicting lovely things in the crystal ball, but I can't tell you about Hurd, because I dropped off shortly after his recitation began, having had a heavy lunch with Whitelaw at the Grand during which he told me some wonderful stories about an old poacher on the Fells, none of which I can now remember.

I hear Maurice has been going round Brixton buying up property. It could be astute, depending on who he's borrowed the money from, but judging by past form I suspect his fingers will get burned along with the various decaying tenements.

Yours among Equals,

DENIS

1 NOVEMBER 1985

Dear Bill,

Sorry to miss your beano at the Goat and Compasses on Friday night, but I have had to take things a bit easy since getting back from the Bahamas. As you may remember, the concoctions they dispense out there in coconut shells with flowers floating in them are pretty lethal and there wasn't much else to do. The D. of E. has a stronger head, but he's much younger than I am. I only wish that eldest boy of his had half his sense. Did you see him on the box? Nattering away about health food and Van der Pump's nonsense apropos the spirit world. I jolly nearly wrote him a stiff note telling him that if he wanted to wise up about the Inner City malarky you and I and the Major would be very happy to give him lunch at the RAC any time for an earful of solid common sense on the 'thinking' of Messrs Yobbo and Coon.

That aside, the Commonwealth shindig went off very satisfactorily from our end of the barrel. I had a letter only this morning from Mrs Kafferbesher saying how pleased they all were with M's line on sanctions, and how right the old girl had been to stand up to what she called 'that crew of brandy-swilling Sambos'. A bit strong, I suppose, but when you've been down there, as I have, and seen the very decent standard of living and nicely cut grass they have, you can understand why they should want to use strong language in order to preserve it. I asked Furniss about the Krugerrand situation, and his view is that we should hang in there – I assume you've still got yours – as they were bound to go up now they possess an additional rarity value. He thought I must have had a hand in banning them, but if I had I certainly wasn't going to go blathering to him about it.

What the pinkoes over here don't seem to have hauled in is that like ourselves Banda and Co all stand to lose a great deal of money if the diamond mines grind to a halt; and whereas a lot of hot air doesn't cost a penny they rather draw the line at actually doing anything. The Boss tried to explain this to Mrs Mandela when she called in the other day, but that sort of woman can't listen to reason, as I realised when she asked us both to kneel in prayer

33

and beg forgiveness for P. W. Botha and his 'tribe of abomination and desolation'. Jolly embarrassing it all was.

Meanwhile Roland Rat, our best-selling publicist, remains a cause for concern. Shortly before midnight the other evening I was disturbed during a cellar check by Mr Munster ringing up in a somewhat desperate state. It seems that all their efforts to put a sock in the Archer mouth have come to naught: apparently he'd just appeared on some chat show and said what a clever and sensitive person Paisley was and why didn't we make him Viceroy of all Ireland? Munster's request to me was that I should take him somewhere quiet and explain to him that it was perfectly all right to have such views, so long as one didn't go blurting them out to all and sundry who might misunderstand them. I asked Munster why me? A silence fell at the other end for a moment. Then he said he'd always admired my own reticence and was sure that Archer would instinctively respect me as a fellow patriot who did not suffer fools gladly. After I'd hung up it struck me that what he'd really meant was that I was a fellow nut-case who knew how to keep it buttoned up, and I'm not having some jumped-up whippersnapper like Tebbit dictating to me on those terms. I did however drop a tactful hint to Margaret over a schooner of sherry the following evening, saying why didn't she sack him, just like we did that PR man Rosenthal at Burmah who went round putting purple hearts in the typists' tea. I managed to get out of the room ahead of the lava.

As you may have seen in the *Telegraph*, the boss has just got back from Washington, where she has been trying to psych up poor old Hoppo before he goes into the ring with the Moscow Mauler next month. The fear is that the aged cowpuncher only understands the High Noon scenario and that when he sees Mrs Gorblimeychev he might think he was in the wrong movie. Apparently they've rigged him up with some kind of two-way hearing aid so the producers can tell him what to say, but he's not getting any younger and he could easily go down on a live transmission. Still, who am I to talk? When old Mother Gandhi's boy was over here banging on about exterminating the Sikhs all through the meat course, I caught myself nodding off several times. I told him afterwards my guru had recommended deep meditation, but he only laughed and said I was 'No end of a jolly old wag', and 'A tophole gent' to boot. Stupid twat.

Yours in a trance,

DENIS

'. . . I was disturbed during a cellar check . . .'

15 NOVEMBER 1985

Dear Bill,

Did you see me on the box during the Annual Outing to Halitosis Hall? I was stuck up in the gallery, crushed between fifteen or sixteen malodorous wogs to whom Mr Nicely Nicely had flogged tickets with a view to interesting them in his forthcoming sale of the Dockyards and Heathrow Airport. They obviously couldn't understand a word of it, hawked and spat throughout, and prevented me from dozing off as I usually try to do.

You could see that H.M. was pretty browned off by her script, and I can hardly blame her. Saatchis have been beavering away at their revamped campaign for 85/86, and put some pretty junior copywriter on to cobbling it together. The general upshot is a high-profile law and order sell with the men of violence dragooned in as the New Argies. 'Walk safely through the streets at night thanks to Thatcher'. Chief Inspector Hurd of the Yard is to be promoted to the Charles Bronson role whoever he is, the man the muggers will go in dread of. Not a very convincing scenario in my view. But then my view needless to say is not sought out by the Corsican Twins as they pore over their software.

The only other shot in the locker is the aforementioned Sale of the Century, with Mr Nicely wielding the gavel. All the nation's assets mercilessly stripped in exchange for ready cash for distribution to Maurice's friends in order to facilitate tax cuts. This, we are told, is the last chance, all other means having collapsed under him. (A propos, you remember that M3 business that everyone used to go on about? It was all dreamed up by some bow-tied flavour of the month from the USA called Friedburger. I always said it was balls and was spat on by all and sundry for saying so. The joke is it's now been decided to flush the whole caboodle, M3 and all the rest down the bog. Wonderful the way these political johnnies go on, isn't it? Most of them would be far happier designing frocks.)

All in all it hasn't been the brightest of times for the Great White Mother. I don't know if I told you some time back, but she

'. . . I was stuck up in the gallery . . .'

spent many hours in the summer ringing up Hopalong and telling
him he'd got to buy some kind of glorified telephone kiosks for
military use that had been dreamed up by our boffins. Very nice,
very cheap, just get his cheque book out, she'd guide his hand.
Blow me, last week, the old cowboy puts down a first instalment
on some Frog version of the same thing, just because Mitterand is
prepared to throw in a 35% discount and a presentation pack of
Parfum de Paris for the emaciated spouse. The Boss was pretty
livid and snatched up the blower to give him an earful. Was this
her reward for years of humiliating acquiescence in all his crazy
schemes, including Star Wars, kidnapping of terrorists in mid-air,
monkeying about with South American guerillas etc? What had

Mitterand ever done? The man was a self-confessed Bolshie, hand in glove with Gorblimov, always laughing at him behind his back and so on and so forth. When she finally put the phone down I pointed out that the old boy probably hadn't had his hearing aid in, so it had most likely been a waste of breath. Just to twist the knife in the wound, Johnny Frog popped up in all the papers next morning to deliver a lecture on the art of salesmanship, blaming M. for the whole thing and putting it down to her overbearing manner. I said next time leave it to Mark and me, witness our success with the Saudis, but at that point the needle on the seismograph began to bend against the little peg at the end of the dial and I deemed it prudent to shimmer down the stairs and away to the Padded Room at the RAC.

I can't join you at the Inner Wheel Strip Aid concert next weekend, as we've got the Bogtrotters coming over to try and patch up some kind of scheme for buttoning Paisley's lip. Nothing will come of this if you ask me. The only way to deal with a great thug like that is to transport him. Let him run some little island off New Zealand with a congregation of Mudmen and Duck-billed Platypi. Old Dr FitzG. who likes a dram as much as the next man and who is a very decent egg, is pretty anxious after what happened last time, when, as you may remember, the Boss led him up the garden path all through the secret talks and then tore up his essay in front of the whole class.

I turned out as per usual for the Cenotaph, only to discover my security pass had expired. I thought of pulling rank a la Raine Spencer, but on reflection nipped round the back and persuaded the Major to slope off early and join me for a couple of blockbusters in Boris's private flat.

Yours at the going down of the sun,

DENIS

10 Downing Street
Whitehall

29 NOVEMBER 1985

Dear Bill,

Sorry I wasn't in when you rang the other night, but I thought it advisable to slip out during the visit of the Orange Lodge, as barking a band of bowler-hatted frothers as it has been my misfortune to glimpse in many a long year. Did you hear that maniac Paisley commending Margaret to the devil? I was rather hurt not to be included in the curse, but he probably thought I was already a slave to Beelzebub as it was. I can't understand what they're so worked up about. All that happened was that nice old Dr FitzG. rolled up to the conflab smelling pleasantly of Jamiesons, they both agreed that things couldn't go on as they were, and that as Hopalong's Bogtrotters over in the States were determined that something be done, why didn't they shunt a few pen-pushers from Dublin up North to sit in on meetings and take things down. I don't know whether you saw the chap with glasses who's in charge there now getting a pretty good mauling from the Prods. It was a scene that put one powerfully in mind of the time Prosser-Cluff tried to shin up the fire escape when the share-holders ran amok at the Burmah Far Eastern Options AGM in Singapore.

According to Boris, the Geneva get-together was all fixed months ago by Saatchiski and Saatchiski, the only purpose of the whole exercise being to sell the new model Bolshevism with a view to pushing their exports in the West. Hopalong played his part to perfection, endorsing the new product with many a grin and squeeze of the hand. Unhappily for the old Rhinestone Cowboy, his tiny spouse went down 6–0, 6–0 to Mother Russia in the Fashion Singles, and the Gorblimov Look is expected to sweep Bond Street in the Spring.

You ask why the extraordinary turnabout on letting the media into Halitosis Hall. If you've seen that monkeyhouse as I have, particularly after lunch, you'd understand why I have been unwavering in my view that the innocent public should be spared the spectacle. What actually happened was that at the end of the summer, when M. was trailing very badly in the polls, even

39

'. . . the visit of the Orange Lodge . . .'

behind Gingernuts, the Corsican Twins opined that it would build her up no end to be seen every night kicking the living daylights out of him on the box. But once he went back to poking the ball into his own net every hour on the hour, the pressure eased and by this time Alberto Saatchi, the fat one, had come up with his new Softer than Soft presentation. This portrays Margaret as the velvet-voiced Carer, a far cry from the Grantham Mauler with her thumbs locked round the Kinnock throat. Luigi Saatchi still favours the Mauler Brand as having a lot of shelf-life in it, and I personally think he is right.

You probably saw the latest Alberto Production on the TV, when Margaret shed a tear for Alderman Alf, my late father-in-law, a crotchety old sod who would have hit it off very well with Paisley. (I always put his meanness and bad temper down to his abstemiousness with regard to grape and grain.) Luigi's counterplot is to bring Margaret in as Hammer of the Rapists, Law and Order Supremo, a woman who will not shrink till every soccer supporter is strung up in his own lavatory paper.

Poor old Kinnock. He reminds me very much of that Greek Johnny who got a job killing monsters, and every time he sliced

40

one head off another popped up and bit him in the arse. I can't remember how it ended. Same with little Pillock. No sooner has he tapped Scargill on the nose, than the nasty little Scouse Trot comes wriggling out of the woodwork, then Barmy Bernie the Black Scourge of Haringey. No wonder the Smellysocks are said to be poring over a secret memo saying they haven't a hope in hell at the next election. So much for my hopes of a few large ones at the Closing Time of Life, putting the feet up at Dunleadin, Dulwich.

Yrs in purgatorio,

DENIS

10 Downing Street
Whitehall

13 DECEMBER 1985

Dear Bill,
First things first. You ask me about the Chamber of Horrors PMs' Reunion Dinner in the presence of H.M. the Q. to celebrate 250 years of Number Ten. We had a bit of trouble with the placement at the top table, as you can imagine. Stockton, as the Oldest Inhabitant, tottered in three quarters of an hour early, clearly expecting to be guest of honour, only to find himself on a low kitchen stool at the end of the table. Heath had let it be known that he would only come if he didn't have to speak to 'that woman', not that he need have worried. Meanwhile Runcie was received by Margaret as if he'd trodden in something. I decided to keep well out of it, and when Wilson arrived, indicating his preferred size of tipple between finger and thumb with a wink to Boris who he seemed to have met before, I recognised a kindred spirit and took him into the pantry on the pretext of showing him how things had altered since his day.

God, Bill, what a bore that man is! He sinks them, I would

concede, with the best of us, and Boris soon surrendered the bottle to save himself the trouble of providing refills. But along the road to Lethe one had to put up with some pretty paralysing reminiscences. Some bird called L.B.J. had pissed in the sink, had I noticed the frayed bit on the Axminster where the Falkender woman had chewed it, stains on the ceiling made by George Brown, it seemed it would never end. 'Oh yes,' he droned on, 'this place is full of golden memories for me, ghosts from the past, if these old walls could speak.' At this he fished out a crumpled sheet of paper from his Moss Bros roll-collared D.J. 'By the way, Den, my wife Mary has written a poem in commemoration of this event, perhaps you would care to hear it while Boris here nips next door and finds another bottle.

> 'Oh hallowed walls of Number Ten
> The sights you must have seen
> So gather all the fallen heads
> To greet your sovereign Queen.'

Luckily at this point Margaret's somewhat raucous tones were heard telling us to put our fags out as the Royal Party was arriving, and I was spared the remaining seventeen stanzas.

Conversation was a bit sticky at the kick-off, but emboldened by the foundation of plum vodka I had already laid down, I turned to His Grace Archbishop Snaggleteeth who found himself between me and a comatose Callaghan. He said he was very upset by the way that Margaret had reacted to his report on Urban Squalor, and would I please explain to her that they'd put in a lot of work on it, years of research by busy Bishops who could well have been doing other things, and for Mr Munster – he didn't call him that of course – to describe them all as Marxists before he'd even read it was jolly unfair. Surely the Established Church of England deserved to be given a hearing? I said it deserved a damn good root up the arse. All these sky-pilots putting their noses into politics all over the world, blowing up bridges and making things difficult for Mrs Van der Kafferbesher. If the C. of E. had any real interest in improving the lot of the Rastas, Yobs and assorted layabouts, they ought to take a leaf out of old Archie Wellbeloved's book when he was a curate in Hackney before the war. You will remember what sterling work he did taking them off on hikes, teaching them to play ping-pong and putting on a very good Gang Show before Christmas. I didn't say that Archie

'. . . taking them off on hikes . . .'

would have done his job a bloody sight better, but I think from the way his Adam's apple went up and down I had made my point. 'I am sure there is a lot to be said for your point of view, Mr Thatcher,' was all he would vouchsafe, and I turned to the other side to try and tell poor old Alec Home a joke about Gorblimov and Hoppo on the moon, but a glazed look came into his eye and I think I may have got the punchline wrong. Either that or he's totally gaga.

Even without all that, life in Colditz hasn't exactly been a piece of cake. The Boss was just congratulating herself on the way the Irish Rabbit had come out of the hat, all being smiles with her and Dr FitzG., when up pops this cove King who took over from Hitler Hurd in Ulster, and says that the Bogtrotters have finally come to heel and seen the light, i.e. that there will never be a United Ireland and Paisley rules O.K. Obviously he'd had a few, but Margaret's never been one to look kindly on mitigating circumstances. King was called into the study, given one of the worst wiggings I can remember, during which his hesitant baritone only once interrupted the soprano aria, and he emerged a broken man to make his confession to the House. Smellysocks had a field day, cries of Resign, all the usual nonsense, the Boss having to get onto the green phone to Dublin to explain to Dr FitzG. that King had had a brainstorm, Northern Ireland was enough to drive anybody barmy and he should be bloody grateful that someone was prepared to take on the job.

Did you see the Lillywhite's Xmas Catalogue? On page 7, there's a pair of Swedish thermal golfing trousers that rather took my fancy, or if you're feeling a bit skint page 22 offers an electronic thing for unscrewing caps on bottles that looks quite amusing.

Yours in anticipation,

DENIS

 10 Downing Street
Whitehall

27 DECEMBER 1985

Dear Bill,
I'd never really focussed on this bruiser Sedgmore who's been stirring it up for Maurice's friends in the Square Mile. (You remember, that banker who lent a lot of spondulicks to his Nigerian friend to make dirty films.) However he could win my Man or Woman of the Year award for describing our plump friend next door as a 'snivelling little git'. Obviously he'd had a few, but all the same it's jolly good to know that not all the Smellysocks side are total morons and that some of them can be very witty when the occasion demands it.

'. . . threatened the chairman with an axe . . .'

All in all it's been a bad time for Matey next door. A couple of weeks back the wogs got into a huddle and decided to have a pre-Christmas Oil Sale. Massive reductions, everything must go etc. This just when Fatso was in the shop window pinning up his attractive Tax Cuts for the Spring. The point was that he'd already flogged off everything that wasn't screwed down to pay for them anyway, so there was nothing left in the Petty Cash to fiddle about with. I ran into him, as bad luck would have it, coming out of Number Eleven, sponging his waistcoat after lunch. I was about to twit him on another mirage fading on the desert air, when he got in first and shouted 'Pissed again, Denis? I'd watch out for Mrs Chalker's Random Death Squads if I were you!'

In my experience tempers often get badly frayed just before

Christmas. It was always the worst time for Prosser-Cluff, and I'm sure you'll remember the year he broke into the fire-fighting equipment and threatened the chairman with an axe because they wouldn't let him have a new carpet for his office. Ditto poor Mr Munster, who's obviously feeling the strain and let little Ginger Nut's ragging get up his nose. Apparently he had to be pulled away in the Lobby by loyal friends before he tried to strangle him. This was all splashed over the Press needless to say, and the Boss took it in very poor part, especially as she'd only recently ticked off Roland Rat for speaking out of turn. Munster was supposed to be Mr Nice, half moon spectacles, better suits etc. What was he doing reverting to his Polecat routines?

Tebbit, who had come to lunch in order to get his poke in the eye, immediately burst into tears and said if the Boss wanted him to go he would go. Jolly embarrassing I can tell you; just the three of us, Munster's shoulders heaving uncontrollably, M. giving him the gamma rays. If it had been you or me, obviously, we'd have skulked off to the Club for a skinful and kicked the cat on the way up to Bedfordshire, but these politicians are birds of another feather. I shall never understand them.

Another casualty of the season has been Brittan, the little cookie-pusher from the Moors who came round to complain he was having his tail twisted by Tarzan and that he wasn't going to stand for it one moment longer. All because of some helicopter firm hoping to be baled out by the Yanks and Tarzan wanting his Euro-friends to have a piece of the action. Apparently the Brittan menage was so upset that his bodyguard went berserk in Pickering or somewhere and started taking pot-shots at passing burglars.

Bad news about the *Telegraph*. Apparently Hartwell, the proprietor, had a very forceful missus who kept the show on the road, and after she pegged it he went into a brown study and rather lost interest. (Strange story, but I suppose that kind of thing can happen.) Enter extreme right some money-crazed megabore from the Land of Maple Syrup waving his cheque-book, Hartwell promptly flogs his birthright, everything he's worked for all his life poured down the sink. Exit left, heirs and assigns biting him in the leg and heaping curses on his head. The old editor's apparently very cut up; sits on a stool in the Club; hasn't really taken it in. It seems a shame when Maurice's friends could easily have got together to keep the old rag flying under British control.

46

See you at the Waggonload of Monkeys on the 29th, and tell the Major he's responsible for getting the cut-glass soldiers drawn up on Mrs McConnachie's bar ready for inspection.

Over and Out,

DENIS

P.S. May Yuletide Cheer afore it goes
Emblazon each and every nose.
D.T.

10 Downing Street
Whitehall

10 JANUARY 1986

Dear Bill,

Don't ask me what's going on. Apparently there's this little whirly-bird company down in Yeovil that nobody's ever heard of run by a friend of Maurice's called Cockup who along with everyone else in Lawson's Britain got into a spot of bother on the liquidity front, just like the *Telegraph*. Along comes Conrad Black Mark II, one Sikorski, offering a helping handful of dollars and saying they'll buy up the whole bang shoot and keep the yokels in employment making Yankee choppers. So far so good. Westland Board thinks it's Christmas, which it is, Chairman brings out the bubbly, Rolls-Royce out of hock, skiing holiday uncancelled, air thick with paper streamers.

At this juncture however, at a lavishly refurbished country mansion near Banbury, friend Tarzan, dozing over the morning's paper, springs to life, and uttering his bloodcurdling cry seizes a length of knotted liana and swings into Whitehall, smelling fresh meat in the shape of Mr Britoil, whose rubber stamp is even then poised over Uncle Sam's Rescue Package. Grunt, growl, snarl, within seconds his yellow fangs are locked in Britoil's throat and the Lithuanian is gasping for breath. Leaving the mangled Minister for Trade and Industry wishing he'd never

'. . . *springs to life and uttering his bloodcurdling cry . . .*'

exchanged his snug chambers in Gray's Inn for life in the jungle, Johnny Weissmuller swoops away from tree to tree alerting the Euro-monkeys to see off the marauding Yanks.

Needless to say, it was not long before Brittan appeared at our front door, dusting himself down, Adam's apple going up and down like a yoyo. Not even waiting for me to leave the room, he launched into an emotional address to the Beak: 'It really is intolerable, Prime Minister, all this was agreed in Cabinet early in December. Do we accept the principle of collective responsibility or do we not? That is the question I must ask you to hold in the forefront of your mind. Please answer yes or no.' I naturally expected a pair of smoking chukkah boots to be all that was left of our friend after this kind of approach, but instead a canny light shone in the Boss's eye, and she began to smile in a way that froze my spine. 'Of course, Leon, I understand that you are hurt, and I am very, very angry indeed about the way Michael has been advancing his cause in public. Very angry indeed.' 'Well, then, Prime Minister, if that is the case, surely the proper course in the circumstances would be to demand his resignation sinny D.A.' (The last bit was rather over my head and was presumably some kind of lawyer's jargon.) This had rather more the effect I was anticipating. 'I hope, Mr Brittan, you are not seeking to influence my decision as to Cabinet appointments, which are my sole prerogative.' Blast of gamma rays, L.B.'s curls begin to smoulder.

Since then bugger all has happened, and if you ask me, the Boss is a) not unpleased to see two of her loyallest lieutenants grappling with one another on the carpet, no one much rallying round to help either of them, and b) hoping that Tarzan, given enough knotted liana, will somehow manage to hang himself. I told her, having seen these things happen over the years at Burmah, that people like Tarzan always mistime their run for the top job and can generally be relied upon to shoot themselves in the foot. Take the case of poor old Fatty Prior. He used to sound off against the Boss. Look at him now, pulling down a King's Ransom at GEC. You or I would say he was in clover, but to politicos it's the Gulag.

Will you tell Maurice I'm very sorry about his Knighthood. I put it forward again knowing perfectly well that it was a non-starter, and it seems to have got through to the final round before some smartarse at Saatchis recognised the name and weeded it out p.d.q. Instead the lucky ticket went to that ghastly little creep Gordon Grease, who used to hover round the Boss at the behest of the Corsican Twins, advising her about hairspray and elocution. What he did to get there in the first place, or indeed to deserve a K. heaven knows, but then look at all the other flotsam the Honours' List has brought up.

I looked into Lillywhite's on the first day of the Sale. Total bedlam. Anything good had gone in the first five minutes, and the only thing left were size 14 Japanese Training Shoes. However I bumped into Squiffy Heatherington's brother who used to be in Bahrein, and we got legless at the RAC.

I enclose Mother Flack's brochure for the summer. You'll see from the photograph they've rebuilt the Thatched Bar after Maurice's fire, and each room now has its own deep freeze. Roll on the hols.

Feliz Nuevo Ano,

DENIS

 10 Downing Street
Whitehall

24 JANUARY 1986

Dear Bill,

As I was saying, you may have seen something in the paper about this Westland Helicopter business. The Boss, who had been letting things run their course, suddenly got pulled up short when the reptiles started saying that she was losing her grip and that Tarzan was walking all over her. The next thing that happened was that they had words at a Cabinet, when the Boss gave him the bone-rotting gamma-rays, and our flaxen-haired friend stormed out in a carefully planned impromptu resignation. Since then he has been on all four channels simultaneously twenty-four hours a day, a foolish thing to do, as people soon get sick of seeing the same face night after night. Look what happened to that Irish Johnny with the dimples who used to be the bee's knees at the Corporation. Now nobody's got a good word for him.

All the same, for a few days things did look pretty sticky from this end, and the Boss, for the first time I can remember,

'. . . Frogs cluttering up the Mermaid . . .'

accepted the Monk's offer of a handful of the Valium tablets which he chews constantly during Cabinet meetings. Tarzan, through his friends in Aerospace, had got wind of a very ratty letter from some old seadog who had dropped in at the M. of D. one afternoon for a tot of rum with some old mates, only to find little cookie-pusher Leon B. sitting on the desk, waving his feet and clearly in petulant mood. Recognising the Rear Admiral the moment he put his head round the door, he tore him off a strip there and then, saying he had no business poking his nose into Government affairs, they were all supposed to be neutral and support the Americans. This made Sir Raymond, as the old salt was known to his cronies, so hopping mad that he immediately scribbled down an account of what had been said on the back of a beermat at the Club, and when the whole thing blew up he wrote a snorter to the Boss, sending it round by hand just as our Lithuanian friend was due to step into the ring for his final bruising bout with the Banbury Flyweight, saying roughly speaking that Leon was talking through his arse.

For a time it looked as if the stage hands were all set to bring down the curtain on the Cookie-Pusher's brief moment of political glory: Smellysocks baying for blood, Heseltine booting him up the backside and so on. But these lawyer Johnnies can bore their way out of anywhere and by the time he'd finished droning away in his oily courtroom style, M. had managed to knobble the seadog, remind him of where his employment came from, and a retraction had been biked round p.d.q. pointing out how easy it was for people in top jobs to put a different interpretation on what the other side had said, particularly after a heavy lunch.

So, pro tem, Matey has survived to fight another day, but if you ask me his bed has been shifted a good deal closer to the door, and the next foul-up that can be pinned on him it'll be the trolley in the small hours. Personally I can never fathom what she saw in him in the first place. You and I have seen that sort of chap in striped pants hanging about those pubs down by the Temple, cadging drinks and boring the pants off anyone stupid enough to buy them one. But the Boss has always been a sucker for adulation, and when he comes round fluttering his eyelashes and saying how jolly super she is you can see her getting silly.

As you can imagine, I had to grit my teeth pretty tightly over the Cloth of Gold lark in Lille. I agree absolutely with the Major on this, who as you know is organising a big protest in Deal about the effect of the tunnel on the environment, i.e. his greenhouse business. I told Margaret that even as things stand the South Coast is being overrun with sex-crazed Frogs cluttering up the Mermaid and buying everything that isn't screwed down. What's it going to be like when there's a train-load of them commuting in every three minutes? But after all this Heseltine rumpus she's determined to show that she's just as keen on Europe as Tarzan and has even given way to Brother Frog's refusal to make it a motorway. Can you imagine it, Bill? However, if you see Maurice, I'd advise caution on his wheeze for building pissoirs all the way to the Old Kent Road. These Anglo-French schemes, thank God, have a way of dying a natural death.

See you at the Oddfellows' do on the 22nd.

Yrs,

DENIS

10 Downing Street
Whitehall

Dear Bill,

Has the old girl finally lost her grip, you ask. From where I'm sitting I'd say the answer was unquestionably yes, but don't say I said so. First she lets Tarzan go rogue without lifting a pair of secateurs to stop him, then she throws herself across the body of Leon Brittan when it's been perfectly obvious all along that the fellow was a wingeing arsecreeper of the worst kind; now she's playing Dumb Crambo and hoping that everyone will forget all about it.

What people can't accept is that she never knew the little cookie-pusher had leaked some damning letter about Tarzan to the reptiles, when the talk in and around her office was of little else for several days. With any normal person I agree this would be incomprehensible, but what no one can haul in is that she never listened much in the past to what other people were saying, and nowadays not at all. So it's perfectly possible that this Ingham character who's on the strength to feed occasional bits of offal to the snake pit in the way of news, shouted in her ear on numerous occasions

'. . . Denis, Earl of Grantham . . .'

53

without it making any impact on her cerebellum. (Even on our honeymoon, I recall, she asked me to put things in writing and shove them under the door, and to this day I've still no proof she ever read them.)

But you can't expect the media to believe the truth even when it's staring them in the face, and the Smellysocks inevitably saw this as another Watergate with M. playing the part of Tricky Nicky, and yours truly supplying the expletives. When Brittan was finally pushed off the sledge the howling only grew louder, and I began to think about ringing Pickford's. However, as has so often happened in the past, stout Kinnock came to the rescue and tragedy was averted with a truly appalling barrowload of Welsh blether. I wonder if you remember the Burmah v. Mobil Directors' Charity Soccer Match at K.L. when the scores were level and a penalty was awarded in the last minute of play against Prosser-Cluff for biting a member of the other team. Our goalie, as I recall, was unsteady on his pins due to over-imbibing, and their inside right, whose name I believe was Beckwith, had only to tap the ball into the undefended net to secure victory. I don't know what he'd been drinking or whether it was the heat, but he came thundering up and gave the pill an enormous root, whereupon it went straight over his head and into his own goal. I don't think it's ever happened before in the history of the game and there was a good deal of laughter before the whistle finally blew. I need say no more.

Now they've set up some kind of Star Chamber to ferret out the facts. Brittan was first on the rack, but even when they'd stretched him twice his natural length all he'd say was 'No comment', much to the irritation of his torturers.

What with all these comings and goings, the Boss is getting a bit short of subs to bring onto the field. The Monk, whose pill consumption, I am told, is now up to four bottles a day, has announced he can't stand it any longer and is going to quit, Mr Munster's into Stoke Mandeville for a respray, and Lawson's tying himself up in knots trying to join the Snake. It's a pretty chronic state of affairs when all talk on our side down at Halitosis Hall is about Hitler Hurd being a blinding genius and the natural successor when the Number 11 bus finally fulfils its terrible tryst with destiny. I don't know whether you've cottoned on to Hurd yet, but he's one of the ones with glasses and used to be at the F.O. and married his secretary, i.e. not much in the way of competition. So my long-cherished hopes of poling into the Waggonload of Monkeys as Denis Earl of Grantham still look pretty much pie in the sky.

Oy vay,

Yours ay,

DENIS

10 Downing Street
Whitehall

21 FEBRUARY 1986

Dear Bill,

I don't know if you ever see the *Mail*, but some double-barrelled woman who bares her soul weekly for the benefit of the upwardly mobile morons who take the rag in regularly was sounding off last week a propos the Boss. 'Enough of this national interest and so forth' was her theme, 'spare a thought for the little white-haired old man who faithfully potters along behind in the Prime Minister's support: is it not time Margaret sacrificed her career, so that this frail old wino can dribble away his few remaining years in the peace of his suburban garden?' (Amazing that people get paid to write this kind of drivel, but that's showbusiness.)

What struck me plumb between the eyes as I chewed over this bangled harpy's musings, cobbled together no doubt over a couple of large pink gins amid the satin sheets, was the total horror of what she was proposing. This idea of the Boss hovering over one from dawn to dusk, enquiring after the consistency of one's egg, offering fresh toast, plumping up the cushions in one's favourite armchair, reading out selections from the *Daily Telegraph*, measuring one's mid-morning drink and so on until the time comes for her to warm one's slippers and finally toddle upstairs patting one's h.w.b. seemed a scenario compared to which the Reaper's entrance was quite a jolly prospect. Besides which you and I know perfectly well that the notion of M. knuckling under, queueing up at Safeway's in a sheepskin coat and wellies is totally unrealistic. She would spend her whole time bullying the nearest thing that came to hand, interfering with our

55

'. . . a scenario compared to which the Reaper's entrance was quite a jolly prospect . . .'

golfing arrangements, fixing up drinks with local riff-raff, and no doubt marking the gin bottle to record one's annual intake. Say what you like about my present way of life, at least the Boss has got other things to occupy her mind, leaving one reasonably free to paddle one's own canoe up the creek of one's fancy. I may as well confess I owe the *Mail* Sybil a real debt of gratitude, for forcing me to confront the realities and realise that retirement is by no means, as Shakespeare says, a consolation devoutly to be wished on anybody.

The Boss herself seems to have recovered a bit of her croc, and has been nipping Kinnock's pins off every time he stands up with something of the gusto of yore. I think dear old Willie Whitelaw must have organised some sort of chain-letter threatening Aids to anyone who breaks the link. Certainly since Brittan went, the postman has been delivering sackfuls of petitions from loyal citizens pleading with the old girl not to abdicate and wishing her a long and glorious reign. Personally speaking, the latest round of musical chairs and the subsequent thump of bum on floor from Tarzan and little Leon have been nothing but a blessing. I only wish Matey next door could have been removed while they'd still got the skip outside. What a prize arse, Bill! You know he's been flogging off the moveables to pay for tax cuts in his budget: now he's decided what the rest of us have known all along, i.e. that with Sheikh Yamani playing silly buggers with the oil price there aren't going to be any handouts anyway. How the ordinary small businessman like Maurice is expected to keep his toupee above water is anybody's guess.

Did I tell you about Charlie Whackett, that used car spiv who fixed up a job for Mark in Dallas? I didn't realise, but I'm apparently on the board of one of his companies. Blow me, weaving one's way through the Duty Free at Miami after some sort of Freebie laid on by C. Whackett Esquire, a sea of reptiles throngs the lounge, all convinced Charlie's been bankrolled by the Mob. Luckily I'd had a few, so I was reasonably fluent, pointing out that Whackett wasn't the sort of name they have in Sicily, and flogging gravel to unsuspecting housewives on the Green Belt is still fortunately a British preserve, even if the company is nominally controlled by a lot of people with funny Italian names living in the United States. I thought it all sounded pretty convincing, and I see the shares went up a penny on my return.

Arrivederci Amico,
D. Thaccia.

DENIS

57

10 Downing Street
Whitehall

7 MARCH 1986

Dear Bill,

Did you see Hailsham has got spliced? Only goes to show what I've always said, i.e. that these lawyers only think about one thing. You might have imagined that at the age of seventy-eight the fires below would have been banked down, but not a bit of it! Randy old sod! As for what she sees in him, it quite honestly baffles me. If you'd spied him in the House of Lords, as I have, fidgeting about on the Woolsack in a cloud of moths, muttering obscenities whenever Runcie gets up, you'd assume he had been prematurely released into the community by one of our more forward-looking asylums.

As to my own matrimonial arrangements, things have taken a somewhat dramatic turn. All hopes that the Boss would be thrown overboard by her mutinous colleagues in the wake of the Westland business have now faded, and she even appeared on the box talking wildly to that ghastly Dimbleby about leading the party into the twenty-first century.

The following day, as it happened, I was due to meet Maurice at the Club to discuss his new application for the hot croissant concession on the M25 Sevenoaks Feeder. The old boy was on a high having just sold off a warehouseful of old hairdryers to some wogs, and insisted on cracking open a magnum or twain of the Club's best Bubbly to celebrate. Rather unwisely, at about a quarter to four, I began unfolding my problems with the Boss a propos retirement, namely that at the age of seventy-plus, the prospect of things going on as they were was looking increasingly cheesy. At the same time, as I think I told you last week, the Dulwich Scenario with M. ladling out cocoa and watching one's every move like a rattlesnake was equally unappealing. What to do?

Maurice immediately ordered another bottle, opened his brief-case and took out a notepad and jar of pills. 'If you ask me, Den,' he mused after some moments of silence, 'you're heading for an early grave, whichever way you go. Take me and Myrtle, for instance.' Myrtle, it transpired, is his Antique Hyperlady. 'She

58

'. . . old poofs in and out all day . . .'

has her little boudoir apartment on top of the shop in Brighton, and if I was living there I would go barmy. Old poofs in and out all day with bits of junk at a hundred per cent mark-up.' I said I knew the feeling. 'Contrariwise, if she was to hang up her clogs and come over to Maidstone all through the week I'd be up the wall. Know what I mean? I said I did. 'Now then.' Maurice made a few diagrams, swallowed a couple of pills, washed them down with a swig of the RAC Mumm, and leant back looking like Van der Pump after one of his mystical visions. 'Got it!' he shouted, pointing at an oblong on his notepad. 'Here's your

Barratt's Dream Home. And here . . .' he indicated the rather shaky outline of a wine-bottle at the other end of the page, 'is your Number Ten Downing Street. Now, Den, what is wrong with her being here, and you being here? She is obviously fulfilling her destiny at the helm of the nation's affairs in the full glare of the arc-lights whilst you, like a loyal consort, are warming the nest down in Dulwich, looking after the garden, making sure there are no break-ins, taking home a bit of paperwork every so often in connection with your many directorships worldwide, Charlie Whackett and so forth. You got a nice bit of property down there in Dulwich, Den. We don't want it to depreciate, do we?'

An hour or two later I found myself putting these arguments, somewhat higgledy-piggledy, under the laser stare. I have no very clear recollection of what she said, but I was aware of a chill draught of hostility and sharp dose of the familiar radiation before the door was slammed and I was left alone. The following day, however, at breakfast, I was astonished when she suddenly peered over her new-style hi-tech *Daily Telegraph,* and piped 'You know, Denis, I think I've had rather a good idea.' She then proceeded to give me the Picarda Plan verbatim, all with a very gracious smile, and conveying the impression that it was only for my own good. This makes me very suspicious. Where do I take it from here? Any thoughts?

The woman who cleans for Matey next door says 16p on a bottle of gin come the Budget, so if I were you I'd get on to your Cash n' Carry friend in Tonbridge before the Black Day dawns.

Yours with an eye on the crystal ball,

DENIS

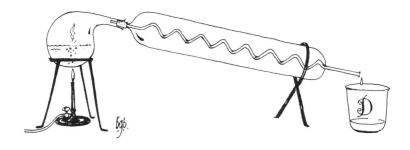

10 Downing Street
Whitehall

Dear Bill,

By the time you decipher this in the corner of the Snug, Mr Nicely Nicely will have opened his lunch box and revealed that there is precious little inside beyond a bag of cream buns and a jar of pate. Still, we have to allow him his hour of giddy triumph once a year in front of the flashbulbs, and I gather he's been down to Swyning's Health Farm in preparation.

You may remember a couple of years ago he was being hailed as M's natural successor, but I'm afraid since then his stock has taken a bit of a hammering, and now you can pick up Lawsons for four and a half pee and still expect to make a loss. Let me give you an example of his superb economic management: as you have probably noticed when you roll into the forecourt of your local gaso, the price of juice has come tumbling down over the last few months. Good news for the small motorist, you might opine, and for Britisles p.l.c. This, however, is not how it looks from Matey Next Door's viewpoint as he tries to peer over his waistcoat. Oh dear me no. If the price of petrol falls, slap an extra half crown on every gallon and bring it up again. Q.E.D.

Meanwhile in the City they're all blind drunk and everything's going through the roof, on the supposition that Fatso is going to bring the interest rates down. Not, according to Friend Furniss at the NatWest, so. 'We shall be damn lucky', he said to me yesterday as he filtered some of the sludge off his home-made Vinho Maloroso, 'if we see half a percent off.' This may be bad news for Sir Terence Beckett and the boys under the boardroom table, but for you and me with our couple of mill. stashed away on deposit, it must be pretty good news. On the other hand, from a more broadly catholic point of view, it might be argued that Mr Nicely's made a pig's arse of it once again. I certainly never thought I'd look back on the days of Mr Mogadon Howe as a golden age.

Munster's taking a lot of stick in the corridors for speaking his mind about this and that, it being the accepted wisdom of the ones with glasses that we should be Wise Monkeys until the

'. . . precious little inside . . .'

election and then play the Nice Old Family Doctor card. Chief of the GP brigade is Hurd, who despite being an utter swine puts on a very good act as Mr Reasonable: 'On the one hand, on the other, keep taking the tablets etc.' Munster prefers a bit of a scrap, getting his teeth in the other chap's leg, the old Tom and Jerry scenario.

Munster is all for flogging off BL to the Yanks, and I must say I agree with him two hundred per cent. Ever since that Metro of Maurice's blew up on the M25 I've had very little time for the dozy buggers on the production line at Longbridge. Heath and Co are all caterwauling about the wonderful British Land Rover, but meanwhile the cunning little Nips are knocking out the Watascorcha version at half the price and with much better ashtrays. Mucky Fairclough has got one down on his farm outside Eridge, and he swears by it. Puts all his pigs in the back of a morning, down to the Berni Inn with Mrs F. and the daughters in the evening: bit of a pong but the pigs don't seem to mind a bit. Of course Heath has never worn a pair of muddy boots in his life, but he'll make a song and dance about any bloody thing to get a rise out of the Boss.

At the eleventh hour, by the way, Maurice P. is trying to form a consortium to buy up BL, and asked me if I'd have a word with Charlie Whackett at Attwood's to see if his Sicilian friends in the Cayman Islands would be interested in a slice of the action. The last I heard of Maurice he'd gone down to Cheltenham with his Hyperlady and ended up in Intensive Care.

What are you doing over Easter? If Daphne's off on one of her jaunts, what say you we go and beat up Mother Flack on the Algarve? Carol dropped off a couple of Package Tour Cheapoes she picked up at the *Telegraph* which mean getting to Gatwick at four in the morning on Maundy Thursday, but the Proles aren't really on the move down there in April, and we'd have the Course to ourselves, if you don't count that funny bloke with one leg – Stringer? Rabinowitz? – who goes round on his own with the lurcher. Let me know either way.

Yours in haste,

DENIS

10 Downing Street
Whitehall

4 APRIL 1986

Dear Bill,
Do you remember that rather pot-bellied friend of Maurice P. who was over here a few years back representing some lager company who threw a big party down at Deal and the marquee caught fire? Ozzie Willis was the name, and I'd completely forgotten he existed till the other morning when Margaret's press man Ingham, a Yorkshire bruiser who used to work for the other

side, came hurrying in as we were breakfasting a deux, with a copy of the *Mail on Sunday*. Some reptiles had dug up a yarn about the Boss owning shares in a company called Broken Down Mines or some such in the outback: it was obviously a lie, should he sue?

M. immediately turned white at the gills with rage and named appropriate damages, calling for Havers on the blower with a view to prosecution for malicious libel. Just then it all came flooding back. After the marquee fire, a whole lot of us had been drowning our sorrows in the Mouse and Anchor, and Ozzie had pulled out a bundle of stock he said was going remarkably cheap; he was a bit strapped for the fare home, were there any takers? Of course we were all near to tears already on account of the fire, so I put down a couple of thou, filled in the Boss's name for a joke and thought no more about it.

As you can imagine, this took a bit of explaining, punctuated as my narrative was by various flying objects. Did I not realise in my childishness I had broken one of the fundamental laws of parliamentary democracy? No political leader was permitted to dabble in stocks and shares. All her life had been lived in the shadow of my murky business connections. She had known all along that one day the vultures would come to roost. I had handed Fulham to the Smellysocks on a plate. How could I bear to go on living as such a despicable human being? When she drew breath I pointed out that contrary to all my misgivings, Ozzie's junk had made a very nice little profit, which would help to pay off the Dulwich mortgage. Petrol to the flames, and I retired badly singed.

All in all it has been a bad time at the Corner Grocery Store. Ever since the solids came into contact with the punkah over the Westland business, she's had her knickers in a knot about Uncle Sam gobbling up BL. I said getting into bed with General Motors was the best thing they could do, but weedier voices prevailed, particularly that of some very rich fat cat called Channon, who seems to be asked along for Cabinet meetings nowadays. Flags were wagged and an attempt was made to stitch up some kind of a compromise whereby we continued to supply the radiator caps and plastic licence holders and pretended it was all as British as the Duke of Edinburgh. In the end the Yanks got pretty brassed off with all the small print and pulled out. So it's back to the drawing board, and unless the Japs hop in pretty soon and make

'. . . *the job was left to some cleaning lady . . .*'

an offer for the bankrupt stock, Maurice could well be in there with a chance.

Meanwhile Havers is Odour of the Month for ballsing up in Dublin. The Garda had finally hauled their arses out of the Shamrock Bar and caught up with the World's Most Wanted Woman living quietly in rented accommodation in Dunleary under her own name, a popular figure at the local Legion of Mary. All Havers had to do was get one of his penpushers to fill in the appropriate form in triplicate, bike it over to the Emerald Isle and bingo – Miss Glenloonie would be behind bars for her natural. Everyone having clearly pushed off for the weekend, the job was left to some cleaning lady who happened to answer the telephone, with the result that Paddy O'Beak at the other end was chuffed to Naafi breaks. Form incorrectly filled in, section 349 not initialled in the presence of an MP or Practising Clergyman, no legal validity, off she goes. A Keystone Kops scenario then ensued in which she was chased once round Dublin, popped back in again and then released, leaving Hurd, M. etc all with a faceful of egg. Plans are now afoot I gather to begin another dragnet-style search to find a lawyer sufficiently competent to fill in the form.

Matey next door is, as you can imagine, cock-a-hoop about his bloody Budget. 'Tailor-made for you, Den!' he shouted across Downing Street as he was dragging his Bunter-like weight into the back seat of the Ministerial limo. 'Not a penny on booze and no Capital Gains Tax on gifts. Now you can be as generous to Mark as you've always wanted to be! Ha ha ha!' With this the door slammed and he was driven off, leaving yours truly breathing fumes.

Yours till we dead awaken,

DENIS

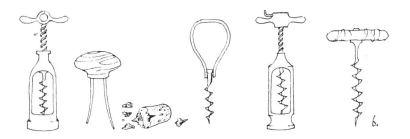

18 APRIL 1986

Dear Bill,

'Is World War Three about to break out?' you ask. The answer is that when you have a battered Hollywood geriatric in a ginger wig like Hopalong in charge anything can happen. The Boss has been on the blower to him several times in the last few days to find out what the hell is going on. In most cases she only managed to raise the male nurse on duty, and when he did come on the line he hadn't got his deaf aid in and repeated his line about 'You ain't seen nothin' yet' over and over again until she hung up. (Did you see, incidentally, that they've elected another of those film stars to mayoral office? What an extraordinary place it must be. I mean we'd think it pretty rum if that Minder man Cole suddenly popped up to take over from Red Ken at County Hall.)

The difficulty about zapping Gadaffi, as we ourselves found out when they started mowing down the constabulary in St James's Square, is that a lot of our highly respected business community, like Maurice's friend Cookie Rusbridger, have got some pretty juicy deals lined up out there building hotels and swimming pools for the Colonel's Revolutionary Committees, and this naturally creates some pressure against using the big stick on the golden goose. I fancy the same thought may have got through to that part of Hoppo's brain that is still functioning. Having lined up his pieces on the board ready for the big strike, he is now all of a dither. Half his Cabinet are pulling him along the Rambo line, while the other half have got their pocket calculators out and are totting up just how much they stand to lose in dollars.

Whatever happens I fear it spells curtains for the Old Cowboy as a credible warmonger, and from now on I think it'll probably be the bathchair out on the porch playing his mouth-organ.

You may have seen that our man came a poor second at Fulham. Needless to say, the Smellysocks have been whooping it up and Glenys has been out choosing soft furnishings for Number Ten, it being the first time they've ever won a seat since

'. . . old Silly Billy himself . . .'

the Boss seized power. Tebbit however has taken it pretty well and after a few large ones in the Boss's den they all came out laughing a good deal and deriding Kinnock as a balding bantamweight. Oddly enough, I don't know if you saw, but the same view of our Neil was voiced in the Italian press by old Silly Billy himself, who having imbibed a couple of bottles of poisoned plonk on a stopover in Italy, plunged the knife into the back of his leader and then came home blaming the interpreter as per usual. This has been seen in the Operations Room at Smith Square as belated Hat in the Ring time.

Tell Daphne I passed on her petition against Sunday Opening to the Boss, but quite honestly, having seen what happens to these pramloads of signatures that are wheeled in daily for Boris to feed into the central heating, I wouldn't recommend it as a means of friendly persuasion. Personally I don't give a fig about Sunday as long as the pubs are open along with the odd off-licence, but the Boss is very keen that money should continue to circulate. However if it's left to Hurd I imagine he can be relied on to balls it all up.

Fancy old Nicklaus pulling it off in Augusta. Just goes to show there's hope for all of us wrinklies. Talking of which Maurice's Club has just installed a new indoor driving range with mixed sauna and bar facilities that he speaks very highly of. Why don't we tool down there one afternoon when the weather picks up a bit? I could offer you a modest lunch at the Club, Boris can motor us down, and we might beat up Dr O'Gooley who's got a love-nest just off the Fourteenth on the way home. He thinks we don't know about it.

Yours a la carte,

DENIS

2 MAY 1986

Dear Bill,

Please apologise to the boys in the Snug if I failed to come across with the inside gen in my last, but it now emerges that all the Brass were under strict instructions not to breathe a word to D.T., he being regarded as 'highly unreliable, especially after eleven a.m.' (This according to Boris's perusal of the files.) So while Mr Mogadon was glad-handing the Euros and telling them they must all stand together for moderation and restraint, knowing perfectly well that Hoppo's wogbusters were already scrambled with the Boss doing her Vera Lynn from the waving base, I myself was still being kept in the dark.

Since then M. has taken a lot of flak from Smellysocks and the Reptiles, and even the new man at the *Telegraph* saw fit to join the chorus of appeasers. Personally I was 100% in favour of taking out Gadaffi socks and all, and what the hell if a few sons of the desert bite the dust in the process? You and I have been out East, Bill, and seen the sort of riff-raff they have in those places. The word bath doesn't occur in the language and most of the day is whiled away in unmentionable activities behind the Pyramids smoking dope and expectorating into the sand. So hats off to the overall concept of the Short Sharp Shock.

Where I could have warned the Boss, had I been privy to her thoughts, was on the question of Hoppo's ability to deliver the goods. It's a sad fact that the Mafia has always done these things a great deal better than the CIA. When I was last in Washington, Charlie Whackett told me that they worked for years on a plot to blow up Castro with an exploding cigar. When he put it in his mouth it wouldn't light, so the CIA agent on the spot showed him how to do it and was instantly blown to Kingdom Come. Exactly the same with this Tripoli lark. In fact, given the fabled accuracy of the USAF, it was a bloody miracle they didn't hit Malta. For a few hours they tried to kid themselves that Gadaffi had met his end, the Army had come out in favour of Western Democracy etc, then up he pops on the telly cool as a cucumber and getting maximum publicity from the carnage. (Incidentally, have you

'. . . so the CIA agent on the spot showed him how to do it . . .'

been watching the BBC? If anyone doubted that the Corporation was controlled directly from Moscow their doubts should now be allayed.)

The trouble is, of course, that the Boss still looks at Hoppo through rose-tinted specs, and where you or I see an old movie actor with dyed hair scarcely capable of finding his arse with both hands, she regards him as someone who's go to the top of the tree in her profession and will therefore do anything for him. It's always sold to Joe Public as a great partnership, but in fact we get bugger all by way of return, witness the Yanks' refusal to turn in the Bogtrotters and now the mass cancellation of tourist bookings by the Blue Rinse Brigade. (A very good thing, in my view. Do you remember all those ghastly lawyers cluttering up the lounge at the Mermaid with their damfool lapel badges and tartan suitcases?)

To conclude, it seems to me the Boss's touching support for the old cowpuncher has not done her a mite of good with the Proles, high though hearts may be among the anti-wog faction in the Cat and Hamster. The fear now is that Hoppo will have another try for Double Top and probably wreck the bar, and where are we to stand in that eventuality? All in all, gloomy do's for our chaps in the upcoming by-elections and Saatchis are already talking about limiting the damage.

I take it we remain undeterred as far as the Algarve is concerned, or do you suspect that Muslim Fanatics will be lurking beneath the thatch of Mother Flack's Hacienda al Pueblo?

Margaret says I've got to take an SAS man along. What about Pranger Hotchkiss? Is he still alive?

Yours hasta luego,

DENIS

Dear Bill,

Thank you for your Gorillagram on the occasion of my seventy-first birthday. It considerably livened up an otherwise mournful occasion, held as it was in the shadow of Margaret's humiliation at the polls. Just the two of us, Munster, and a funny little johnny with a speech impediment and loud socks who used to be something big at the *Telegraph* before this new Canadian chappie took over. Mr Wu had got a virus and was laid up, so one of Margaret's secretaries put something in the microwave in the upstairs flat and we all had to pretend the Boss had been slaving all day over the stove.

I couldn't help feeling a bit sorry for the old girl. She got back from the Land of the Rising Yen very bushy-tailed indeed, Hopalong's praises ringing in her ears for the tough communique putting Gadaffi well and truly beyond the pale, and tickled pink by a set of mediaeval thumbscrews given her by Old Bandylegs the Emperor. Then slap bang wallop, they're off, and every one of our hot tips comes a cropper at the first fence. They

'. . . it considerably livened up an otherwise mournful occasion . . .'

had of course been expecting to do badly, the Corsican Twins having hoisted storm cones weeks back, but the Boss was not prepared for the demolition of all the splendid work done by General Galtieri. Hence Munster's presence at my birthday wake, summoned by M. an hour early 'so that we can have time for a little chat before dinner.'

Do you remember seeing that dogfight at Littlestone when the Major's Rotweiler went for Mrs Parker-Bowles's Irish Wolfhound and Maurice had to stop it with a fire extinguisher? I was forcibly reminded of that confrontation as Tebbit shaped up to the Boss over the Ministry of the Environment Sherry and Twiglets. 'I always said Cecil should have returned,' she began, 'he had just the right touch. So warm-hearted, so sympathetic, so very much the gentleman.' I must have allowed my jaw to drop rather loudly at this, as she turned on me to administer a brief blast of gamma rays. 'You men were all against him. Just because of some trivial peccadillo long, long ago.' 'Come now, Prime Minister,' Tebbit misguidedly interposed in the clipped tones of the Sergeants' Mess, 'You know perfectly well . . .' 'Don't perfectly well me, Norman. Such a light in his eyes! That man was an inspiration to every housewife in the country.'

Munster drained his beaker of brown fluid and I could see his hackles beginning to rise. 'I blame myself,' the Boss went on, 'I should never have appointed you in the first place. It wasn't fair to bring in a sick man to do a responsible job. I have been talking to Alberto Saatchi and we both agree that you are far too abrasive, uncaring, unshaven and visually sinister to present our case to the nation. What is more, your attacks on our opponents have not only been crude and unpalatable. They have backfired.'

'Now, just a minute, P.M.,' Munster growled removing his half-moon spectacles and wiping them on his shirt-tail, 'if we are to bring personalities into this, let's not forget your own efforts in that department. Your attacks on our opponents have been much more crude and unpalatable than mine have. It is your hoity-toity uncaring image which has lost votes up and down the breadth of the country. Go into any tobacconist, ask any cabdriver, and they will say the same. 'That woman is so bossy she makes my wife look like Mary Poppins.' I swear those very words were said to me only this morning by the man who delivers our barbeque briquets.' Luckily the ex-*Telegraph* johnnie chose this moment to shuffle in, his dayglo socks dazzling us all, and we settled down to a grumpy exchange of pleasantries,

Brother Munster taking the opportunity of leaving shortly after ten with the words 'Ah well, somebody has to run the country.' I do not think he will be with us long.

As if that wasn't enough, Brer Biffen popped up on the goggle-box on Sunday to plant his hat pin between the shoulderblades, his argument being that the Boss should share the load a bit more, and give the Wets a fair crack of the whip. I don't think he'll be with us much longer either.

Margaret prowls around the house, biting her lip and muttering about no surrender, but I did take the opportunity to toddle down to Dulwich at the end of the week to see how friend Tremlett is getting on with the sunlounge. I foolishly allowed Maurice to supply the double-glazing, and Tremlett says it's all warped and that the moisture is building up between the panes. The cellar how-ever is looking good, and I have already transferred those crates of Glenfiddich we were given by that kind Saudi who wants to build a Heliport in Green Park.

Must awa,

DENIS

10 Downing Street
Whitehall

30 MAY 1986

Dear Bill,

Sorry if I bit your head off when you rang on Thursday night, but it was the Mad Monk's farewell party and the mood was pretty lugubrious.

M. had suggested that a few friends should gather quietly to pay their last respects to the architect of two electoral victories and winner of the Min. of Ag. Marketing Department Golden Award for Most Eggs Thrown at any living politician. The poor old bean is in a pretty tense state, clearly a prey to delusions of Trotskyite weirdoes looming behind every curtain, and knocks back the pills by the handful, washed down with a little mineral water. So he was in no position to drown his sorrows with the rest of us. The list of mourners dwindled throughout the day, as M's old guard dreamed up more and more implausible excuses for not showing and in the end it boiled down to a very disgruntled Munster, and Hailsham who hobbled in on his sticks for a good gloat. After a few schooners of Boris's Bulgarian Amontillado he began doing that funny squeaky laugh of his, and rose to his feet to propose a toast to the twitching ex-Minister. Goodbye, Mr Chips — ho ho ho — not the most popular master in the school — ha ha ha — nickname of Mad Monk undeserved, all have our funny ways — hee hee hee — some of us have more stamina, don't find ragging by the boys a problem, but all the same, Common Room won't seem the same without his egg-encrusted mortarboard hanging on its accustomed peg — wha wha wha. Even I could see that this was not going down well, either with the Monk, who was dabbing at his nose with a handkerchief and reaching for a fresh drum of tranks, or with the Boss, who had switched on the exterminator rays and was flicking them about the room in a dangerous way. However, when you get to Hailsham's age, I imagine you don't notice that kind of thing.

The old buffer pressed on regardless, boring away about Dark Days in the past, Tories' amazing capacity for recovery etc and winding up with a lament about declining standards in the calibre of lawyers. M. then cut him short by agreeing with his last point, saying that if Havers knew his arse from his elbow he'd have had the job years ago and wouldn't have to hang around strip clubs with Lord Longford.

The new man at Min of Ed is another one with glasses called Baker, who Saatchis say looks very good on TV. Luigi says he has a caring face, and Alberto has kitted him out with a pair of new specs to enhance the effect. This, it is thought, will help to counteract the effect of Munster. The new broom at the Environment is a very sound man by the name of Ridley, who has done sterling work at Transport getting rid of a lot of country buses which are such a hazard to the motorist trying to overtake on blind corners. I told Margaret he wouldn't have any truck with these butterfly-hunting hippies who try to stop motorways going through some Godforsaken bit of bog, and get under the feet of property developers who are doing their best to provide decent amenities for our lot. Do you remember the trouble the Major had when he wanted to knock down that old barn and put up a high-rise? Every kind of weirdo came out of the woodwork to lodge an objection. In the end he was forced to set fire to it and claim the insurance.

'. . . a toast to the twitching ex-Minister . . .'

Am I expecting to go to this Royal Wedding in July, your wife asks. I realise it's the same day as Fruity P's Masonic drinks party, but we haven't had a stiffie yet, and M. snaps at me whenever I mention it, being rather overwrought on account of trailing Gingernuts in the Marplan. The D. of E. told me, entre nous, that he's jolly glad to have the little bugger off his hands, and this Fergie girl at least hadn't been in any dirty films, even though her mother did a bunk with an Argie. If only we could find some similarly well-upholstered floozy to wed the boy Mark, but suppose it's easier if you happen to be royal and not a thousand per cent prat.

I hope Maurice told you about our little Bank Holiday brush with the Boys in Blue.

Mind how you go,

DENIS